**Amgueddfa Genedlaethol Cymru
National Museum of Wales**

Cardiff 1986

Welsh
Coal Mines

This booklet has been written by Dr. W. Gerwyn Thomas of the
Department of Industry at the National Museum of Wales.

Acknowledgements for permission to reproduce photographs are due to: *The Illustrated London News* for plates 10 and 11; Mr. W. E. Jones, Pontypool, for plates 12a, 12d, 13 and 14; Swansea Public Libraries for plates 21a and 21b; the National Coal Board for plates 31a, 31b, 32a, 32b, 36, 40a, 40b, 41, 42, 45a, 47a, 47b, 48, 49a, 50a, 50b, 52, 54b, 57a, 57b, 58a, 58b and 59. The remaining photographs are from the Museum collection.

WELSH COAL MINES

Wales has two coalfields, the South Wales Coalfield extending nearly 90 miles, from St. Bride's Bay in the west to Pontypool in the east, and the North Wales Coalfield, extending from the Point of Ayr in Flintshire south-eastwards to Hawarden and Broughton, near Chester, and then southwards to a few miles below Oswestry, a total distance of 45 miles.

The South Wales Coalfield, much the larger of the two, is an elongated, oval basin of Carboniferous rocks which is completely exposed, that is, the coal measures outcrop all round its periphery, except for two areas in the south-west which lie beneath the sea of Swansea Bay and Carmarthen Bay. Its width from north to south varies from a maximum of 16 miles in the main part of the coalfield, between Pontypool and Ammanford, to four miles, at the most, in the detached part of the coalfield in south Pembrokeshire. The Pembrokeshire field is very disturbed and although as many as 19 collieries were working there in the 1850s, these were mainly small concerns, and after 1903 the industry declined, until in 1914 only four collieries remained. In 1948 the last one was closed.

In the main South Wales coal basin the strata dip from all sides towards the centre but there are also minor folds, the most important of which is the anticlinal system running east-west from Risca by way of Pontypridd and Maesteg to Aberafan. The effect of these anticlines is to bring up to within reasonable distance of the surface many important coal seams, which would have otherwise been very expensive to reach.

Along the greater part of the North Crop the seams dip gently and as a result the outcrop of the Middle and Lower Coal Measures is comparatively broad, a factor which influenced the location of the great ironworks development of the late eighteenth and early nineteenth centuries, particularly in mid Glamorgan and north-west Gwent. Here both coal and ironstone were abundantly and easily available by simply digging for it, hence the patches and scourings along the heads of the valleys which can still be seen.

On the South Crop, the measures dip steeply, making mining operations more difficult, but the proximity of the coal measures to the sea in south-west Wales had an important bearing on the development of coal mining in this area from the thirteenth century onwards. The output of the South Wales Coalfield in 1855 was approximately 8½ million tons. The next half century or so was one of intense development, culminating in an output of approximately 57 million tons, or one fifth of the total output of the United Kingdom in the peak year of 1913. The South Wales output gradually fell to 45 million in 1930, more rapidly to 35 million in 1939 and even more rapidly to 20 million in 1945. It increased to 24–25 million during the 1950s until 1957, after which it began to fall again. In 1974, the output was approximately 8½ million, practically back to the 1855 level.

The South Wales coals vary widely in range from the best anthracite to the prime coking coals and include the famous dry steam coals, the coking steam coals and the best metallurgical coking coals – the latter, incidentally, is not mined in any other part of Britain except Durham. Some higher volatile coals also occur along the south-eastern edge of the coalfield.

In 1913 there were 620 coal mines, including small mines, working in the South Wales Coalfield employing 232,800 men. At the end of 1975 there were 42 mines administered by the National Coal Board, employing 30,800 men, and 80 small licensed mines employing 600, still in production.

The North Wales Coalfield occupies a crescent-shaped area extending from the north of Flintshire, southward through Denbighshire and into north-west Shropshire. The coal measures are exposed, that is, outcrop, on the west side of the coalfield, but to the north-east they pass underneath the Dee Estuary and to the east they extend beneath a covering of newer strata of the Cheshire Plain and are continuous underground with the Lancashire and Staffordshire coal measures. The coalfield is divided into two parts by the Bala Fault, and in the northern, Flintshire section, the coal measures appear only in a narrow coastal strip, now mostly worked out. The only surviving colliery, Point of Ayr, has an unusually favourable field under the Dee Estuary. South of Flint considerable reserves have been abandoned and flooded after working the Main Seam only. In the main Denbighshire field, which is a maximum of nine miles in width, the depth of the coal measures increases rapidly towards the east so that the area available for development is limited.

The output of the North Wales Coalfield remained consistently between 2¼ and 3 million tons from 1870 until 1906 after which it increased to 3½ million in 1913. It fell below 3 million in 1932 and gradually to 2½ million in 1940 with a sharp drop to approximately 2 million in 1941. By 1974, only two collieries were working, namely Point of Ayr in the north and Bersham in the middle of the Denbighshire field near Ruabon, with a total output of approximately ½ million tons per annum. The North Wales coals are mostly high volatile, medium to strong caking coal.

1

1. Lead and Coal Mines at Mostyn, Flintshire 1684.
The illustration, reproduced from T. Dineley's *Progress of the Duke of Beaufort through Wales, 1684*, probably represents the oldest known drawing of early operations connected with mining. It shows the method used by Sir Roger Mostyn for draining his coal mine or 'coalwork' by means of a water wheel which, through a cog and pinion arrangement, operated a continuous chain in the mine shaft.

2. Coal Works near Neath, 1798.
The horse gin was one of the most common methods of winding employed in the shallow Welsh pits of the eighteenth century. In this artist's impression, the pit is located inside the thatched building and the winding is effected by the horse moving in a circle and rotating the horizontal drum on which the rope is wound. Inside the hut the rope passes over vertical pulleys placed over the pit.

3. Brynpwllog or Rogers Pit.

This water balance pithead gear is seen in its original position at Rhymney in 1934, before it was dismantled and brought to the National Museum, Cardiff, where it stands today. The pit was probably sunk before 1850 to work initially the shallow ironstone veins of the locality, and later coal. The balance gear was worked by placing water in a tank under the empty tram on the surface, while the tank under the full tram at the pit bottom was left empty. On releasing the brake, the full tram and empty tank were raised to the surface and the empty tram and tank of water were lowered to the bottom where the water would be run off, usually to a drainage adit, or otherwise pumped back to the surface. The operation would then be repeated in the reverse order and so on. This method of winding was very common in South Wales during the first half of the nineteenth century.

4. Cwmbyrgwm Water Balance Pit.

Situated at Abersychan, Gwent (SO 251 033), this is the last water balance winding gear that remains in its original position. At one time, in the first half of the nineteenth century, there were more than 60 of these machines in use in Glamorgan alone and probably as many in Monmouthshire. The Cwmbyrgwm pits, of which there were four, date from at least 1820. Only two of them are now traceable – the one with the balance gear, and the other without – the latter consists of the top few courses of stone-work only, forming the oval-shaped shaft which was the common practice in those days in South Wales.

5.   Pwll Phil Rees.
This was another early nineteenth
century water balance pit which was
located near the Ynysfach Ironworks,
Merthyr Tydfil. The headgear is
shown covered for protection
against the weather.

6.

6. Scott's Pit.

This building, which can be seen today from the M4 (Morriston By-pass) at Llansamlet (SS 698984), housed a Cornish pumping engine. The pit was sunk in 1770 by a Captain Scott who soon found himself in trouble from water and abandoned the undertaking. He returned to it a few years later and installed the Cornish beam pump and winding engine to complete the sinking of his pit. Unfortunately, Captain Scott's financial resources were by then so depleted that he could not develop the colliery. He sold it to his friend, Charles Smith, who operated the colliery for its short working life from 1819 to 1838. The author is seen standing on top of the pit in which the pumping rods suspended from the beam were operated.

7. Cornish Pumping Engine House, Grove Colliery, Stepaside.
The colliery was sunk by the Pembrokeshire Coal and Iron Company in 1856 to provide coal for their Stepaside Ironworks, and was situated on the slope of the Stepaside Valley above the ironworks (SN 138076). The photograph was taken in 1969.

8.

8. Brombil Coal Level, Margam, Port Talbot.

Coal levels were opened in Cwm Brombil as early as 1777–80 by the English Copper Company to supply fuel to their copper smelting works at Taibach. Another level was opened by the Company in Cwm Brombil in 1814. The Brombil Colliery was enlarged after the Taibach Copper Works was taken over by Messrs. Vivian & Sons in 1838 until it was producing three-fifths of the coal used at the Works in 1842, which amounted to 500 tons per week. The colliery's underground workings eventually linked up with those of the Goytre Colliery in Cwm Dyffryn and in doing so penetrated under the hills overlooking Taibach for a distance of a mile and a half.

9. Yard Level, Tredegar.

Opened in 1802, this was one of the first levels to supply the Tredegar Iron Works with coal for the furnaces. It was situated in what was known as the 'Top Yard' of the Works and its entrance can still be seen today. Although it had ceased to be used for coal production by 1873, it was maintained as a drainage adit.

From the photographs, taken in 1964, it can be seen that the dry-stone walling and track made of cast iron tramplates were still in good condition. Further inside the level there were still a few of the original trams to be found as shown.

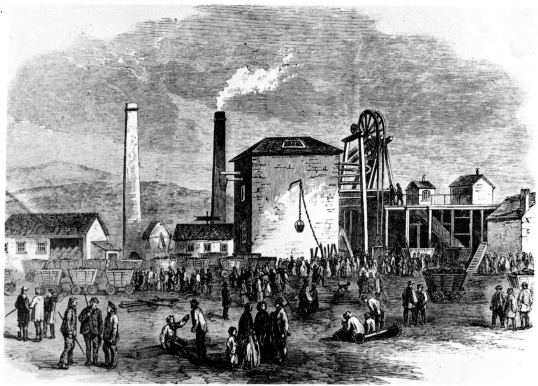

10. Morfa Colliery, Port Talbot.

This colliery, sunk in 1847–49 by Messrs. Vivian & Company, owners of the Taibach Copper Works, suffered an explosion in October, 1863 when 39 lives were lost. An *Illustrated London News* artist visited the scene of the disaster and while he was sketching at the pit's mouth, the search for the missing men was still being pursued and coffins were being held in readiness in an adjoining building as shown in the illustration.

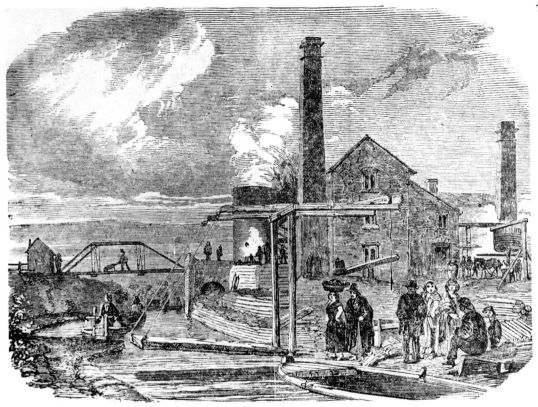

11. Middle Duffryn Colliery, Aberdare. (SO 031 003).

Thomas Powell, who gave his name to the Powell Duffryn Company, followed his initial success in sinking to the Four Feet Seam of steam coal at Trifounder in the Aberdare Valley in 1843 by further sinkings, including Middle Duffryn in the late 1840s. The colliery suffered an explosion in 1850 and another in May, 1852 when 65 men and boys lost their lives. The latter explosion was caused by gas igniting at the ventilation furnace. The furnace stack can be seen in the illustration. The colliery was located alongside the Aberdare Canal, now the new road between Mountain Ash and Aberdare.

12a.

The building shown housed a
vertical steam winding engine with
an overhead flat rope drum, which
wound in the two shafts simul-
taneously. The colliery was started
by Capel Hanbury Leigh in the
1840s. The winding engine was
built at the Neath Abbey Engineering
Works in 1845 and it was in regular
use until 1932 when the pit ceased
production. A beam pumping engine
house (not shown) is located to the
right of the two shafts.

12b.   Winding engine house, Glyn Pits, 1966.
The single cylinder vertical steam winding engine with overhead flat rope drum is still virtually intact and, together with the building, are to be preserved in situ.

12c.   Beam pumping engine house, Glyn Pits, 1966.
The Cornish type beam pumping engine was also made by the Neath Abbey Engineering Works in 1845 and this, again, is to be preserved on its original site.

12d.

**12d. Undercutting or 'holing'
in the coal at Glyn Pits,
c. 1900.**
The collier, using a mandrel or pick,
would cut into the bottom of the
seam to a depth of at least three feet
for the length of his stall as a
preliminary operation to breaking
down the coal. This was later done
by a coal-cutting machine and
today, in the mines worked by the
National Coal Board, the coal is both
cut and loaded on to a conveyor by
a power-loading machine. Shallow
mines were often allowed to use
'naked lights' – candles, for example,
since there was no methane gas or
firedamp found in them. Nowadays
safety lamps are used in all British
coal mines.

13. Filling coal at Plasycoed Level, Pontypool, 1902.
The tram, standing at the coal-face end of the stall roadway, is being filled by the collier's assistant using a curling box. No shovels were allowed for filling coal in those days as their use caused too much small coal (and stone) to be filled, for which there was no sale.

14. Notching timber at Baldwin's Level, Pontypool, c. 1900.
The collier in the days of pillar and stall mining, in addition to cutting and filling coal and setting props at the coal face, had to support his stall roadway with sets of timber. Each set consisted of two arms, one on each side of the road, joined by the collar which went under the roof. The photograph shows the timber being prepared and in this case a notch is being cut at one end of the collar. A similar notch would be cut at the other end and the two arms would be wedge-shaped at the top to fit into the notches at each end of the collar.

15.

16. Tynewydd Colliery, Porth, 1877.
Sunk in 1852 by the Troedyrhiw Coal Company, the Tynewydd Colliery was situated alongside the Rhondda Fawr river near its junction with the Rhondda Fach at Porth. In April, 1877 the colliery was the scene of a flooding disaster when 14 miners were trapped by an inrush of water from adjacent old workings of the Cymmer Colliery. Five of the men lost their lives and four were rescued 18 hours later, leaving the remaining five, who had taken refuge in a rise heading. Their presence was discovered four days after the inundation when the rescuers heard their knocking through a 40 foot wall of coal. A party of volunteers immediately began cutting a small tunnel through the coal barrier. Eventually, on the tenth day, the rescuers broke through to the trapped men after some anxious last days when accumulated gas and water threatened the lives of both the entombed men and the rescue party. The latter's heroism was recognised by the award of the Albert Medal, hitherto bestowed only for gallantry in saving life at sea.

15. Newbridge or Gelliwion Colliery, Pontypridd.
The first steam engine used in the Rhondda was that erected by John Calvert at his Newbridge Colliery in 1845. This small beam engine was used for pumping and winding, the winding being done by flat chains with wooden blocks driven through the links. The engine is now preserved in the grounds of the Polytechnic of Wales, Treforest.

17a.

17. Cymmer Colliery, Porth.

The first photograph (c. 1860) shows the New Cymmer Pit, which was sunk by George Insole in 1855 alongside his Cymmer Old Pit, sunk in 1847. In the foreground is the River Rhondda. In 1856, the colliery suffered the worst explosion in this country or abroad up to that time when 114, out of the 160 men and boys working underground, were killed. By 1877, George Insole had deepened his New Cymmer Pit, replaced the wooden headgear with an iron lattice structure and added a new upcast shaft in order to exploit the steam coal. The second photograph shows the colliery soon after the completion of these new developments. In 1914, Cymmer Colliery employed 2,331 miners and it continued in production until 1940.

17b.

18a. Penrhiw Colliery, Pontypridd.

Situated at Pen-y-rhiw, three quarters of a mile from Pontypridd, the Penrhiw Pit was being operated in the late 1890s by the Great Western Colliery Company which worked the No. 3 Rhondda Seam. By 1900 there were 280 employed at the colliery and the manpower climbed gradually until it reached a peak figure of 636 in 1919. The workings were abandoned in 1922 after which the pit was retained for pumping purposes only. The wooden headgear, the last one remaining in the coalfield, was dismantled in 1964. The winding engine eventually became redundant in 1969 and was presented by the National Coal Board to the National Museum of Wales for preservation. It has since been dismantled and transported to Cardiff where it is in storage until required for a future stage in the Museum's development programme.

18a.

18b. Horse haulage in a South Wales coal mine, c. 1910.
In 1913, the peak year for output, there were 17,744 horses employed underground in the South Wales Coalfield. In 1974 this total had diminished to 144 — made up of 71 in N.C.B. mines and 73 in licensed mines.

18b.

The Garn Pit Blaenavon. June 21st 1890.

19. Garn Pit, Blaenavon, June 21st, 1890.

This colliery was sunk by the Blaenavon Ironworks Company prior to 1839. The illustration shows that the colliery was ventilated by a furnace — as shown by the additional squat stack — and that naked lights were used in the form of the peg and ball oil lamp worn in the cap. Also much in evidence is the bowler hat, worn mainly by the 'gaffers', and the water jacks and food boxes.

20a. Court Herbert Colliery workmen, Skewen, 1898.
Situated a short distance to the east of Neath Abbey, Court Herbert Colliery was probably developed very near the site of one of the earlier Neath Abbey collieries started by Richard Parsons in 1793. It was being worked by John Parsons in 1854, but in 1886 he relinquished the colliery to the Dynevor Coal Company, who managed it until the Main Colliery Company was formed in 1892. The colliery, which employed 249 in 1895, rising to 371 in 1918, ceased working in January, 1929 when the Main Colliery Company closed down.

20b. Court Herbert Colliery screens, 1913.
Generally it was the older or partly disabled men and young boys of 12–14 who were employed to pick out the stone from the run-of-the-mine coal. After 14, the boys would usually be transferred underground as colliers' assistants.

DEFNYDDIWYD Y BEIBL YMA MEWN CYFARFODYDD GWEDDI
A GYNHALIWYD BOB BORE LLUN O DAN Y DDAEAR
YNG NGLOFA MYNYDD NEWYDD ABERTAWE. FE'I DEFNYDDIWYD
YN GYNTAF YN Y FLWYDDYN 1871 AC YN GYSON HYD 1932
PAN GAUWYD Y LOFA.
THIS IS THE BIBLE USED AT PRAYER MEETINGS HELD
EVERY MONDAY MORNING BELOW GROUND AT THE OLD
MYNYDD NEWYDD COLLIERY SWANSEA. IT WAS CONTINUALLY
USED FROM 1871 UNTIL THE COLLIERY CLOSED IN 1932.

21. Mynydd Newydd Colliery, Forest Fach, near Swansea.

Sunk in 1843, Mynydd Newydd was owned initially by the Swansea
Coal Company and then from 1866 by Vivian & Sons who owned
copper smelting works as well as several collieries in the Lower Swansea
Valley. An explosion in 1869 caused the death of three miners and as a
result of this tragedy the men decided to establish a chapel underground
in the Six Feet Seam lying at a depth of 774 feet. A chamber was hewn
out of the solid coal and supported by timber along the sides and in
rows across. The roof and sides were whitewashed and rough plank
seats placed between the rows of timber. There, every Monday
at 6 a.m. for the next 60 years, until the colliery closed in 1932, a
service was held before the men proceeded to their working places.
The illustrations are from an article in the *Sunday Magazine,* 1899.

22a. Brynhenllys Colliery directors, c. 1890.
Probably opened in 1872, this anthracite drift mine proved a great success. The colliery was situated on the Brecknock side of the upper reaches of the River Twrch which formed the boundary between the former counties of Brecknockshire and Carmarthenshire. The colliery's name, Brynhenllys, was taken from a nearby farm where, it was said, courts were held in olden days.

22b. Water wheel at top slant, Brynhenllys Colliery, c. 1890.
Brynhenllys Colliery at one time in its history had three water wheels in operation, providing power for various purposes at both the Top Slant and the Lower (Old) Slant and pumping pit, as well as for a brickworks. At the top left of the photograph can be seen the wooden trough which carried the water to the wheel and at the top right is the roof of the engine house. The water wheel drove the slant winding engine and a surface compressor as well as operating pumping rods connected to a ram pump at the bottom of the slant.

23. Maindy Colliery, Ton Pentre, 1967.

In 1864, David Davies of Llandinam, in his 46th year, diverted his restless energies from railway construction and lime quarrying to exploiting the mineral resources of the Rhondda Fawr. He and his partners leased mineral property and started sinking at Maindy and Cwmparc, but 15 months later, after the expenditure of over £38,000, there was no sign of coal. Consequently, David Davies, according to his biographer,* called his men together one Saturday morning early in 1866 and said 'Well boys, I am sorry to tell you that I cannot go on here any longer. I am very sorry, for I believe there is some grand coal here and that we are close to it.' He paid the wages due and when he had finished he observed, 'That leaves half a crown in my pocket.' One man shouted, 'We'll have that too.' David Davies tossed it towards him, saying contemptuously, 'Take it,' and he walked away. After he had left, the men discussed the position and decided they would give him a week's work for nothing.

On the Friday of that week, March 9, 1866, one of the finest seams of coal in the world was struck at the Maindy Pit at a depth of 215 yards. It was the Two Feet Nine Seam of steam coal and a little later the Four Feet was met at 230 yards and the Six Feet at 253 yards. The Cwmparc sinking followed suit soon afterwards and David Davies & Company went on to sink a further two pits in the Rhondda and one each at the head of the Ogmore and Garw Valleys. In 1885–6 the Lady Windsor Colliery, Ynysybwl was sunk and in 1887 David Davies & Company became the Ocean Coal Company, Ltd., which, after the acquisition of Deep Navigation Colliery, Treharris, in 1893, produced a total output of $2\frac{1}{4}$ million tons per annum. Maindy reached its peak manpower of 1,399 in 1894. The average manpower during the early years of this century, however, was from 900 to 1,000. This figure fell suddenly to 215 in 1931 due to the economic depression and from the mid-1930s until it closed in 1948, Maindy employed approximately 350 men.

*Thomas, Ivor, *Top Sawyer,* London, 1938.

24. Deep Navigation Colliery, Treharris, c. 1910.

Known originally as Harris's Navigation Pits, after the principal shareholder, who also gave his name to the village which grew up around the colliery, the Deep Navigation shafts were the deepest at the time in South Wales. They were 760 yards deep to the Nine Feet Seam, 200 yards deeper than any of the other collieries in the coalfield. Sinking started in October, 1872 and the two shafts were completed in May, 1878.

The photograph shows the workmen grouped around Major David Davies, M.P., Chairman of the Ocean Coal Company, and his family. In the left background is the South Pit winding engine house, and the building on the right housed the huge Cornish pumping engine with its 100 inch diameter cylinder which pumped from 760 yards depth in eight lifts. Major David Davies, later Lord Davies of Llandinam, was the grandson of David Davies, founder of the Ocean Company. The colliery, in 1976, is in its 98th year of continuous and profitable working, producing the best quality Welsh steam coal.

25. Deep Duffryn Colliery, Mountain Ash.

Sunk by David Williams, Ynyscynon, in 1850, Deep Duffryn is the oldest working colliery in the coalfield. It was purchased in 1857 by John Nixon who, within two years, increased its production from 150 to 1,000 tons per day. He installed the latest equipment, including more powerful winding engines, together with his own patent ventilating apparatus – one of the earliest mechanical ventilators in the country. The first photograph shows the colliery in 1884 with the original wooden headgear and on the extreme right can be seen part of the upper chamber of the Nixon Ventilator.

The second photograph shows the colliery as it is today, viewed from the same vantage point. Day shift miners are seen walking from the pit over the same bridge, on their way to the lamproom. The wooden headgear was replaced in 1888 by a wrought iron lattice structure which was designed by Nixon and made at his Navigation Colliery foundry and workshops. The main members of the headframe, which is still in use today, consisted of lengths of bull-head rails bound together at intervals with wrought iron bands riveted to the rail flanges (25d).

The third photograph is of the Waddle Fan at Nixon's North Pit (ST 050990), which, until a few years ago, served as a stand-by ventilator for Deep Duffryn Colliery. It is hoped to preserve it since it is the last remaining one of its type in the coalfield.

26. Bwllfa Dare No. 1 Colliery, Aberdare.

Opened in 1859 by Ebenezer Lewis, the colliery, which is at the head of the Dare Valley at Cwmdare, was known originally as Bwllfa. In 1866 the owners were the Bwllfa Colliery Company Ltd., and in 1871 the colliery was taken over by J. Brogden & Sons. During the 1880s its name was changed to Bwllfa Dare. In 1890 the Bwllfa & Merthyr Dare Steam Collieries (1891) Ltd. took over the Cwmdare collieries including the Bwllfa Dare or Bwllfa No. 1 as it became known.

The colliery ceased production in 1936 but was retained on a maintenance basis in connection with Bwllfa No. 2, lower down the Dare Valley. In 1949, the National Coal Board began a large reconstruction scheme to combine Bwllfa Dare or Bwllfa No. 1 with Mardy Colliery at the head of the Rhondda Fach. This combined unit is still working today. The photograph shows the colliery in the early 1900s with a wooden headgear and the squat stack of the ventilation furnace. The latter was located in an underground roadway, near the bottom of the upcast shaft as illustrated.

27a.

27b.

27. Western Colliery, Nantymoel, Ogmore Valley.

Sunk during 1872 by David Davies & Company, Ocean Western, as it was popularly known, was soon in production and gave rise to the village of Nantymoel. The colliery was merged with Wyndham Colliery in 1965 and the combined Wyndham/Western Colliery, employing 1,188 men, produced 474,874 tons of saleable coal in 1970/71, the highest output in the coalfield. The illustrations show the colliery around 1910 and in 1967 with the underground stables in the Two Feet Nine Seam. The Western Colliery was initially ventilated by two furnaces at the bottom of the upcast shaft which are marked on plans of the old Six Feet Seam workings.

28. Avon Colliery, Abergwynfi, Afan Valley.
Located at the head of the Afan Valley, the Avon Pits were sunk between 1877 and 1882 by Sir Daniel Gooch and others. The colliery worked the steam coal measures including the Six Feet Seam lying at a depth of 496 yards and in 1905 it was taken over by the Great Western Railway Company. Its manpower had reached 907 by 1909 but fell to a mere 30 men in 1910 and remained at this maintenance level for the next few years. During this period it was bought by the Ocean Coal Company which, three years later, in 1915, had re-started production at the colliery. The Ocean Company operated Avon until nationalisation and the colliery was finally closed by the National Coal Board in 1969. The photograph, taken in 1950, shows the two shafts, one on each side of the narrow head of the valley.

29. International Colliery, Blaengarw, Garw Valley.
Two pits were sunk by the International Coal Company Ltd. in 1883, and by 1899 there were 916 men employed at the colliery, including surface and underground workers. In 1910 a third pit was sunk and the colliery also worked the No. 2 Rhondda Seam by means of a level which worked until 1923. In 1928 the colliery was taken over by Glenavon Garw Collieries Ltd., Port Talbot and in 1937 there was a further change in ownership when the colliery came under the control of the Ocean Coal Company Ltd. through a newly-formed subsidiary, the International Colliery Company (Blaengarw) Ltd.

The photograph, dated 1952, shows International Colliery on the left and behind it the village of Blaengarw, at the head of the valley with the Garw Colliery just visible on the right. Both International and Garw Collieries were controlled by the Ocean Company in the early 1940s and had a ventilation system partly in common. International was closed by the National Coal Board in 1967 but the Garw Colliery is still working today.

30. Ferndale Nos. 8 and 9 Pits, Tylorstown, Rhondda Fach.

The Ferndale Nos. 8 and 9 Pits were the southernmost of the Ferndale group of collieries of D. Davis & Sons, Ltd., and was the last of them to be developed. The No. 8 Pit was sunk to the Six Feet Seam, a depth of 456 yards, in 1894, and became the largest of the Ferndale collieries, employing 1,145 men underground in 1918. The under-manager, the man in charge underground, at the No. 8 Pit from 1894 until 1918 was David Griffiths, who, when he retired after 50 years' service, was presented by the officials and workmen of the Company with an illuminated address as shown, and a wallet of Treasury notes. His wife received a silver tea service. The No. 8 Pit ceased raising coal in 1935, but No. 9 carried on until 1960.

The second photograph shows the two pits (No. 8 is on the left) in process of demolition in 1967.

31. Mardy Nos. 3 and 4 Pits, Maerdy, Rhondda Fach.

In 1873, Mordecai Jones, a native of Brecon and a typical example of the pioneer Welsh coal owner, bought the mineral rights of the Maerdy Estate at the top end of the Rhondda Fach. He took another Brecon man, Wheatley Cobb into partnership and the sinking of the Mardy Nos. 1 and 2 Pits was started in 1875 and reached the Abergorki Seam in December, 1876. In 1877 the owners were described for the first time as the Locket's Merthyr Company and in the following year the Nos. 1 and 2 Pits were deepened to reach the valuable steam coals, including the Two Feet Nine, Four Feet and Six Feet Seams.

From then on the enterprise prospered greatly, but not without great cost in human life, however. In 1885, 81 persons lost their lives in an explosion. This kind of tragedy was repeated in many South Wales mines, particularly during the second half of the nineteenth century when there were 37 explosions each involving the loss of more than ten lives. The underground workings of the Nos. 1 and 2 Pits had become extended by 1893 when the Company decided to sink the No. 3 Pit. This was followed in 1914 by the No. 4. Both pits were about a mile further up the valley than Nos. 1 and 2. The latter ceased production in 1932 after Locket's Merthyr Collieries Ltd. were taken over by the Bwllfa & Cwmaman Collieries Ltd. The Nos. 3 and 4 Pits, in turn, ceased production in October, 1940 but were kept on a maintenance basis until the late 1940s when the National Coal Board embarked upon a major modernisation scheme involving the construction of a completely modern colliery on the site of the Nos. 3 and 4 Pits. The scheme included the driving of roadways underground to connect up with the underground workings of Bwllfa No. 1 Colliery, two and a half miles away over the mountain at the head of the Dare Valley. Mardy was the first combined mine project to be undertaken by the National Coal Board in South Wales. The photographs show the colliery before and after reconstruction.

32. Tŷ-Trist Colliery, Tredegar.

Located at the southern end of Tredegar, the Tŷ-Trist Colliery started operations in 1834 when the Nos. 1 and 2 Pits were sunk by the Tredegar Iron Works Company. (Another pit, the Upper Tŷ-Trist, was sunk in 1841.) In 1868 the No. 3 Tŷ-Trist (Fan Pit) was sunk and the Tŷ-Trist No. 1 Pit was deepened from the Elled to the Old Coal Seam.

In 1873, the Tredegar Iron Company's interests were transferred to the newly-formed Tredegar Iron and Coal Company Ltd., which put more emphasis on coal production for sale purposes and embarked on a considerable modernisation scheme for most of its 20 collieries in the Tredegar area. The number of persons employed at Tŷ-Trist continued to increase, and stood at 1,220 in 1910. By this time it had outlived all of the original Tredegar Iron Works collieries except one, and by the time it closed in 1959 it had outlived all its predecessors in the South Wales Coalfield, having been active for 125 years. The photographs show the colliery in 1947, the year when the coal mines of Great Britain were nationalised.

POCHIN COLLIERS ENTERING POCHIN TRAIN FOR TREDEGAR

33. Pochin Colliery, Sirhowy Valley.

The Tredegar Iron and Coal Company, after its formation in 1873, embarked on an intensive programme of colliery sinkings starting with the Whitworth Pits at the lower end of Tredegar, which were completed in 1876. In May of that year the ceremony of cutting the first sod for the Pochin Pits, about three miles south of Tredegar, was performed by Miss Pochin, daughter of one of the company directors after whom the colliery was named. Sinking was suspended after reaching the rockhead and it was not resumed again until the end of 1880. After re-starting, sinking proceeded with greater rapidity than was ever previously recorded, and the large diameter, 340 yard deep pits, were completed in ten months. Coal was first raised at Pochin in 1881 and it became one of the most extensive of the Tredegar collieries, employing 1,696 men in 1910. The Pochin colliers' train at this period (before pithead baths) must have been an impressive sight when it disgorged its several hundred passengers amid clouds of coal dust on arrival at Tredegar. The second photograph was taken in 1964, soon after closure.

34. Bargoed Colliery, Bargoed, Rhymney Valley.
In 1897 the Powell Duffryn Steam Coal Company Ltd. started sinking
to the steam coal at Bargoed and the Rhas Las or Nine Feet Seam was
struck at a depth of 625 yards in November, 1901. The two steam coal
shafts are 21 feet in diameter and by 1903 a separate shaft, 18 feet
in diameter, was sunk to the Brithdir Seam of housecoal which was
reached at a 200 yard depth. The Bargoed Colliery was developed
rapidly and in 1910 there were 1,943 miners employed in the North and
South (steam coal) Pits and 678 employed in the Brithdir (housecoal)
Pit.

The photograph shows the three Bargoed pits with the Brithdir Pit on
the left. Also illustrated is the scene at pit bottom at the end of the
shift in the Brithdir Pit in 1910 with the miners waiting to ascend. The
trams are filled well above the rim, that is raced, with lump coal. On the
left two trams, containing hand-picks or mandrels, are on their way up
to the blacksmith for sharpening. The Brithdir Pit was closed in 1949,
but the North and South Pits are still working today.

35a.

Senghenydd.

35c.

35b.

The Welsh Pit Disaster. Where over 400 Miners were entombed. Tuesday Oct. 14th 1913.
Scene after the second fire broke out

35d.

35. Universal Colliery, Senghenydd.

Located at the head of the Aber Valley near Caerphilly, the Universal shafts were started by the Universal Steam Coal Company in 1892–3 and were completed in 1897 at a depth of nearly 650 yards. The colliery was developed rapidly and employed 1,612 men in 1910 working the Four Feet, Six Feet and Nine Feet Seams of prime steam coal. Taken over by Lewis Merthyr Consolidated Collieries Ltd. in 1905, the colliery suffered the worst disaster in the history of British coal mining when 439 miners lost their lives in an explosion on the morning of Tuesday, October 14, 1913. The first two photographs show the village of Senghenydd with Universal Colliery in the background and the crowd gathered at the colliery surface after the disaster. The other photographs show further scenes at the pithead during the following days. The colliery was closed in 1928.

35e.

Welsh Pit Disaster. A little mother waiting for news.

35f.

"Universal" Pit Senghenydd. The Canary that was carried down the Mine to test the air. Benton 132 George St Glasgow. 10.

36. Point of Ayr Colliery, Ffynnongroew, Clwyd.

This colliery is situated on a reclaimed headland near the mouth of the Dee Estuary. The first trial borings were drilled in 1865 under the instigation of Lord Mostyn, owner of the Mostyn Colliery, which was then producing 300 tons per day. Two of the bore holes proved good workable seams and in 1866 the Prestatyn Coal Company was formed to work the coal proved at Point of Ayr, but for some reason the project was abandoned.

In 1873, a new company, The West Mostyn Colliery Company, was formed and sank the No. 1 Shaft to a depth of 100 yards from where a heading was driven which struck a fault and further development was abandoned. The shaft lay derelict until 1883 when, following a report on the colliery, another company, The Point of Ayr Collieries

Company, was formed which de-watered the shaft and explored in another direction when the Five Yard Seam was struck. In 1890, having proved the Three Yard and Two Yard Seams, No. 1 Shaft was deepened to 215 yards and a second shaft, No. 2, was sunk to a similar depth. From then on the colliery has been worked successfully and profitably and is still working today.

In 1921 there were 476 employed at the colliery which was the second largest in the Flintshire coalfield at that time. In 1953, with a manpower of 738, its annual output was approximately 213,000 tons, and until that year, when the colliery was reorganised, some of it was regularly shipped from the colliery's wharf as shown in the photograph which was taken in 1948.

37. Gresford Colliery, Wrexham.

Sunk by the United Westminster and Wrexham Collieries Ltd. between 1908 and 1911, Gresford became one of the largest collieries in the North Wales Coalfield. In 1921 there were 22 coal mines working in Denbighshire and 18 in Flintshire. The largest of the Denbighshire collieries was Hafod employing 1,943, followed by Gresford with 1,653, and there were another four employing over a thousand men. In 1933, Gresford, with 2,244 men, was second in size to Llay Main with 2,770.

On September 22, 1934 there was an explosion at the Gresford Colliery as a result of which 262 miners and three rescuers lost their lives. This was the worst disaster in British coal mining since the explosion at Senghenydd in 1913. An extensive fire followed the explosion and the mine was sealed off the following evening. All the men not accounted for were presumed dead. Only 11 bodies were recovered and the pit remained sealed for six months after the explosion. Sections of the mine, except the Dennis district where the explosion took place, were then gradually recovered and coal production was resumed from January, 1936. Gresford continued working until it was closed by the National Coal Board in 1972 due to exhaustion of reserves.

38. Bersham Colliery, Rhostyllen, Wrexham.

Started by the Bersham Coal Company in 1864, Bersham was idle for six years until it was re-opened in 1871 by Messrs. Barnes & Company who deepened the shafts to the Main Coal. After 1879 the colliery was owned by the Bersham Colliery Company Ltd. until 1912, when it was taken over by the Broughton & Plaspower Coal Company Ltd., who operated it until 1922, when the ownership reverted to the Bersham Colliery Company Ltd. In 1936, the colliery was again taken over by the Broughton & Plaspower Coal Company Ltd., who retained control over it until nationalisation in 1947. In 1971, Bersham's 770 miners produced 1,100 tons of saleable coal per day from the Queens and Ruabon Yard Seams. The mine, which is still working today, is fully mechanised with power loaders and self-advancing roof supports.

39. Elliot Colliery, New Tredegar, Rhymney Valley (SO 144028).
The Powell Duffryn Company was formed in 1864 and its assets
included the New Tredegar Colliery which had been started at least
ten years previously by Thomas Powell. The company continued the
development of New Tredegar Colliery and in 1883, having leased
further mineral property to the south of it, they began sinking the
Elliot Colliery shafts – first the West Shaft and in 1888 the East Shaft.
Elliot Colliery became one of Powell Duffryn's most productive
collieries, reaching its peak manpower of 2,811 in 1912. The colliery
remained with Powell Duffryn until nationalisation and continued
working under the National Coal Board until it was closed in 1967.

There were two steam winding engines working at the colliery until
it closed. Both were the last in their class and since it was possible to
preserve only one, the choice was a very difficult one. It was decided
to opt for the East Pit winder which is a twin tandem compound engine
made by Thornwill and Warham. The date on the engine house is 1891
and this building, which is practically all that is now left on the
colliery site, has been taken into guardianship by the Department of
the Environment, while the National Museum of Wales has responsib-
ility for the engine.

40. Penallta Colliery, Hengoed, Rhymney Valley.

The Powell Duffryn Steam Coal Company, continuing their policy of expansion, followed the Bargoed sinking with the sinking of the two Penallta Pits which was started in 1906. Sufficient space was available at Penallta to enable the company to lay out the surface buildings on the most modern lines with one large central engine house for the two winding engines, compressors and generators, and another large building for all the work shops. The Penallta Nos. 1 and 2 shafts were 783 and 750 yards deep respectively and were both completed in 1909.

The colliery's manpower rose gradually, reaching a peak figure of 3,208 in 1931. It was one of the few collieries in South Wales to install, in the late 1940s, the Meco-Moore Cutter-Loader, one of the first power loaders to be adopted in British mines. The photographs, taken in the early 1960s, show the colliery surface and the interior of the power house with steam winders and turbo-generators which disappeared with electrification in 1962-3. The colliery is still working today.

41. Llanbradach Colliery, Llanbradach, Rhymney Valley.
Pneumatic picks were introduced into South Wales collieries in the mid 1920s to assist in the cutting of coal previously done by mandrel, bar or hammer and wedge. The use of pneumatic coal picks increased greatly during the late 1930s and early '40s until in 1944 a fifth of the coal produced in South Wales was obtained by this means. It then became necessary to devise some means of suppressing the dust caused by these picks. What became known as the 'wet pick' was eventually introduced. It directed a water spray on to the coal being worked by the pick. Such a pick is shown being used in the early 1950s at Llanbradach Colliery which worked from 1894 until 1961 and which, at its peak in 1913, employed 3,000 miners.

42. Marine Colliery, Cwm, Ebbw Fawr Valley.
The Ebbw Vale Steel Iron and Coal Company Ltd., and the Blaenavon, Tredegar and Rhymney Companies, developed their coal mining activities greatly in the late nineteenth century. In 1889 the Ebbw Vale Company sank the Marine pits which were completed to a depth of 414 yards in 1891. The colliery soon employed a large work force which continued to increase during the early part of this century, reaching a peak figure of 2,728 in 1919.

In 1935, the Marine, along with the Ebbw Vale Company's other collieries, including Waunlwyd lying just above it in the valley, were sold to Partridge, Jones & John Paton, Ltd., who worked them until nationalisation. Waunlwyd was merged with Marine in 1964, after which the surface installations at Waunlwyd were demolished. Marine is still working today, the last colliery in the Ebbw Fawr.

43. Six Bells Colliery, Abertillery, Ebbw Fach Valley.
In 1892, John Lancaster & Company extended their coal-mining activities down the valley of the Ebbw Fach with the sinking of the Arail Griffin Colliery at Six Bells. Coal production was started a few years later and by the early 1900s the colliery, along with several others in the Ebbw Fach, was in full swing, producing steam coal, prime coking coal and house coal.

In 1914, Arail Griffin reached its peak manpower of 2,857 and in 1936 the colliery was taken over by Partridge, Jones & John Paton Ltd., who worked it until nationalisation. The colliery, by then known as Six Bells, was the scene of an explosion in 1960 when 45 miners lost their lives. It is still working today. The photograph shows miners emerging from the pit at the end of the day shift.

44. Navigation Colliery, Crumlin, Lower Ebbw Valley.

In 1907, Partridge, Jones & Company Ltd. started sinking operations at the Navigation Colliery which were completed in 1911. No expense was spared in the construction of the surface buildings or in the plant and equipment placed in them. There were two steam winding engines, and the one at the North Pit was one of Markham's latest designs at the time. There were also two triple expansion fan engines made by Walker Bros., Wigan, one of them serving as a stand-by.

Crumlin Navigation was taken over by the National Coal Board in 1947 and continued working until 1967–8. One of the huge fan engines, with its 16 foot diameter, 15 ton weight pulley-flywheel, has been preserved for eventual exhibition at the National Museum of Wales's new Welsh Industrial and Maritime Museum in Cardiff.

45. Celynen South Colliery, Newbridge.

In 1873 the Newport-Abercarn Black Vein Steam Coal Company Ltd. started sinking the Celynen Pits. Three shafts were sunk, Nos. 1 and 3 for winding and No. 2 solely for ventilation. The first coal was raised in August 1876. By 1905 the colliery's manpower stood at 1,740, the output was 10,000 tons per week and the working faces in some districts were two and a half to three miles from the shaft.

The method of working was by longwall heading and stall and in one district, the Main East, which had a seven foot thick seam of coal, there were as many as 110 stalls or working places at 12 yard intervals extending for a distance of three-quarters of a mile. Horses were used to take the coal out from the stalls to a junction with a main haulage road from where the coal was taken by rope-haulage to the pit-bottom. A steam winding engine was used to raise the coal up the shaft and, as shown in the photographs of the colliery in the late 1960s, there was a steam winder still working at Celynen South, as the Nos. 1, 2 and 3 Celynen became known. It was taken out in 1970.

46. Big Pit, Blaenavon.
Sunk in 1860 by the Blaenavon Iron and Coal Company to increase their coal production for sale purposes, the Big Pit became the coal winding shaft for the earlier Coity Pits which were used thereafter for ventilation purposes only. The photograph shows the colliery surface as it is today, the second oldest working mine in the coalfield. Other contemporary scenes at the colliery show a 'bond' or cage full of men reaching the surface at the end of the day shift, the self-service lamproom, the pit-head baths and the canteen.

46c.

46d.

46e.

47. Nantgarw Colliery, Taffs Well.

In 1910, Thomas Taylor started sinking the two shafts of Nantgarw Colliery which were completed in 1915 to the unprecedented depth for South Wales at that time, of 856 yards. The owners, described as Taylor's Navigation Steam Coal Company Ltd., employed 866 men at the colliery in 1923 but sold out to the Taff Rhondda Navigation Steam Coal Company in 1924. The latter, due to the adverse geological conditions prevalent in the base of the Caerphilly Syncline, gave up in 1927 and in the following year sold the colliery to Powell Duffryn Ltd.

It remained idle for a number of years until a scheme for re-opening the mine and working it on the horizon mining system was submitted by the company and approved in 1946 by the Ministry of Fuel and Power. The adoption of this scheme was made more practicable by the advent of nationalisation in 1947 which permitted areas of coal to be worked from the Nantgarw shafts not previously owned by Powell Duffryn. The reconstruction of the colliery was duly completed and it is still working. The illustrations show the colliery's reconstructed pit-head and the interior of the all-electric winding engine house.

48. Glyncorrwg Colliery, Glyncorrwg, Cymmer (Afan Valley).

The Glyncorrwg North and South Pits were sunk by the Glyncorrwg Colliery Ltd. to a depth of 417 and 403 yards respectively in 1904. By 1910 there were 567 persons employed at the colliery working the No. 2 Rhondda (North Pit) and the Six Feet and Nine Feet Seams (South Pit). In August, 1912 Glyncorrwg became idle and remained so until 1919 when only the South Pit was listed, employing 144 men and working the Red Vein. In 1926, the colliery was acquired by Glyn Neath Collieries Ltd., and in 1927 they were employing 384 men, working the Nine Feet and Peacock Seams which were classed as anthracite. In 1928 the Amalgamated Anthracite Collieries Ltd. took over Glyncorrwg which marked the eastern limit of the anthracite coalfield. The manpower increased to 995 in 1938 and the colliery continued working for a number of years after nationalisation until its final closure in 1970. The photograph shows the colliery in 1953 before the reconstruction carried out in the late 1950s and early '60s.

49a.

49. Blaengwrach Colliery, Cwmgwrach, Neath Valley.

After the completion of the Vale of Neath Canal in 1795 and its extension to Giant's Grave, near Briton Ferry, in 1799, there was a surge forward in the development of collieries in the Valley. Among these early collieries was the Blaengwrach Colliery at Cwmgwrach where developments in 1814 included opening out ancient levels since this was a very old mining area. In the nineteenth century there were a number of private owners and companies involved here, among them were Edward Protheroe, the Aberdare Iron Company and N.V.E. Vaughan.

Then in 1898, Empire Collieries Ltd. started the Empire Colliery by re-opening Protheroe's old Cwmgwrach Levels and sinking a new shaft. In 1908 a new company, the Caerbryn and Empire Collieries Ltd. was formed and a new level, the Six Feet or Cwmgwrach Level, opened, while the Empire workings were abandoned. The company's title changed in 1914 to Cwmgwrach and Empire Collieries Ltd. and in 1918 a further shaft was sunk at Cwmgwrach. In 1924 the old Level Fawr was re-opened and by 1927 a new level, Level Newydd, had been opened and the Cwmgwrach Colliery then employed a total of 966 persons. In the late 1950s, the colliery underwent a major reconstruction resulting, in 1962, in the

Blaengwrach New Mine. The scheme included a new level drift from a point on the surface near the Aberpergwm washery.

The first photograph shows a haulier leading a horse pulling a tram out of the Cwmgwrach No. 1 Level in the early 1950s. In the Blaengwrach New Mine, where the Six Feet Seam of anthracite coal is worked by full mechanised methods, the coal is shown being brought out by locomotive which starts its journey from a point one and half miles inside the mine.

50. Steer Pit, Gwaun-Cae-Gurwen.

Gwaun-Cae-Gurwen is situated well inside the anthracite belt of the South Wales Coalfield and although it has a history of coal working dating from the early seventeenth century, the first pit was not sunk until 1837 by the owner Charles Morgan. It remained in the Morgan family until 1874 when it was sold to a number of Yorkshiremen who formed the G.C.G. Colliery Company. The original pit, afterwards known as the Old Pit, was provided with a beam winding engine and flat rope drums until 1886. The G.C.G. Colliery Company sank the Maerdy Pit in 1886, the East Pit in 1910 and the Steer Pit in 1924, all of them at Gwaun-Cae-Gurwen.

The first photograph shows Field Marshal Montgomery talking to the workmen and their families at the Steer Pit during his tour of South Wales in 1947. The second photograph is a general view of the colliery in 1952.

51. Ammanford Colliery, Amman Valley.

The Ammanford Little Vein or No. 2 Slant was opened in 1891 according to the date shown above the arched entrance. The slant was driven through highly inclined strata and then through a fault, at 120 yards from the mouth, and it eventually reached the Little Vein with an average gradient of 1 in 4. The Little Vein at Ammanford is three feet thick and the No. 2 Slant reached in a distance of 1,300 yards. The owners, the Ammanford Colliery Company, employed 573 persons at the No. 2 Slant in 1921, but in 1924 the Company was absorbed by United Anthracite Collieries Ltd.

In 1927, the largest combine in the anthracite field, Amalgamated Anthracite Collieries Ltd., had control of the colliery and held it until nationalisation. The No. 2 Slant is still working today, but will be replaced in the near future by the Betws New Mine, located higher up the hillside where the Red Vein outcrops and where two new drifts are being driven to exploit reserves of this seam beyond the old workings of the Ammanford No. 1 Slant.

The photograph, taken in 1975, shows a journey of full trams being drawn up No. 2 Slant by rope haulage. Ammanford is one of the last of the anthracite slants where this method of raising coal to the surface is still used.

52. Pantyffynnon Colliery, Ammanford.

The photograph shows hand-cutting and filling-in the Stanllyd Seam at another anthracite drift mine just south of Ammanford during the 1960s. In 1961, Pantyffynnon produced 134,742 tons and employed 601 men. It was closed on January 31, 1969.

53. Saron Colliery, Ammanford.

The photograph shows the ceremonial cutting of the first sod for this colliery. Started in 1915 by the Blaina Colliery Company Ltd., Saron Colliery was one of several slants driven on the north crop of the anthracite belt of the coalfield. These slants were often driven to the dip in a particular seam and then across the measures to develop other seams. Saron was taken over by Henderson's Welsh Anthracite Collieries Ltd. in 1928, and in 1936 the colliery reached its peak manpower, employing 384 persons. It was closed by the National Coal Board in 1956.

54. Pentremawr Colliery, Pontyberem, Gwendraeth Valley.

This colliery is one of several in the Gwendraeth Valley that were driven from the surface where the seams of anthracite coal outcrop along the Gwendraeth Fawr river. The latter in effect forms the western edge of the main South Wales coal basin, since the Pembrokeshire part of the coalfield lies further west across Carmarthen Bay.

After an abortive start in 1870, when two slants near Pentremawr Farm struck a fault, another slant was driven near the adjacent Capel Ifan Farm which proved several seams. Eventually four slants, known initially as Capel Ifan Nos. 1, 2, 3 and 4 were driven to develop the Gwendraeth, Braslyd, Gras and Trichwart Seams at the colliery. In 1913, a new slant, the Pumpquart No. 4 Slant, was driven to exploit the Pumpquart Seam. In 1924, Pentremawr Colliery employed a total of 1,007 persons and in 1927, the Pentremawr Colliery Company Ltd. was absorbed into the Amalgamated Anthracite Combine.

The first photograph, dated 1912, shows the colliery officials grouped outside the new Power House. Due to a geological fault, the Big Vein at Pentremawr was not discovered until 1939. It has since proved a great boon to the colliery so that although the Pumpquart No. 4 Slant was closed in 1968, the colliery carried on successfully working the eight foot thick Big Vein by hand-got methods and raising the coal to the surface at the No. 3 Slant until the early 1970s — even after the colliery had been integrated with Cynheidre. The second photograph shows the afternoon shift ready to descend the Pumpquart No. 4 Slant in 1955.

54b.

**55–56. Small Mines: Blaencuffin, Llanhilleth; Big Arch,
  Abersychan.**

The Coal Industry Nationalisation Act, 1946, vested all the collieries of
the United Kingdom in the National Coal Board as from January 1,
1947. Just over a third of the collieries were small mines, employing up
to 30 men and most of these were granted licences by the Coal Board
which allowed them to continue operating under their working
proprietors.

In December 1975, 80 small mines operated in South Wales. One of
them is Blaencuffin which works the Mynyddislwyn Seam and another,
the Big Arch Mine, which works the Meadow Vein. Small mines are
invariably worked from the outcrop and access is by level or slant.
They commonly work pillars of coal left from previous workings so
that their life is limited to a few years. The method of working is
usually by the old heading and stall system with timber supports; the
coal is worked by hand — sometimes assisted by shot-firing or by
pneumatic pick — and then filled into trams. These are pushed out to
within reach of the haulage out of the mine, which, in the case of a
level, is by horse, as shown at Blaencuffin, or, in the case of a slant,
by rope, when a few trams are raised at a time as shown at Big Arch.

57. Abernant Colliery, Rhydyfro, near Pontardawe.
Situated halfway between Gwaun-Cae-Gurwen and Pontardawe,
Abernant Colliery was one of two large new anthracite sinkings
undertaken by the National Coal Board in the 1950s. The other was
Cynheidre in the Gwendraeth Valley. The Abernant sinking was
completed to a depth of 897 yards in 1958 and the surface layout can
be seen to incorporate all the most modern colliery design features
such as landscaping, the efficient and compact arrangement of
buildings and the latest equipment for winding (tower mounted friction
winders), together with adequate office accommodation, pithead baths,
canteen and car parking facilities. In 1972, 1,020 men produced
365,000 tons of coal from virtually 100 per cent mechanised workings
in the Red Vein Seam. The photograph, taken in 1968, shows a
Trepanner Power Loader at work on one of the Abernant coal faces.

58. Brynlliw Colliery, Grovesend, near Swansea.

Sunk between 1903 and 1905 by Thomas Williams (Llangennech) Ltd., Brynlliw is located in the dry steam coal belt and initially worked the Swansea Four Feet Seam lying at a depth of 340 yards. This seam is only two feet two inches thick at Brynlliw and in 1914 the underlying Five Feet Seam (two feet ten inches thick) was developed. The colliery ceased production in 1925 due to a depression in trade and was abandoned in 1927 but the shafts and headgear were retained.

In 1954 the National Coal Board embarked on a major project to re-open the colliery which entailed repairing the shafts and deepening them by 35 yards, erecting new headgear with skip winding in the Upcast Shaft, and driving several thousand yards of tunnels underground for locomotive haulage. The reconstructed colliery was in production by 1961 and initially worked the Swansea Six Feet Seam by mechanised room and pillar methods. By 1968 Brynlliw was working the Three Feet as well as the Six Feet Seam, both now classed as anthracite, by fully mechanised longwall methods.

The photographs, taken in 1969, show the colliery surface and a coal face in the Six Feet Seam equipped with a disc shearer power loader and powered roof supports. Unfortunately, this seam, which varies in thickness from three feet one inch to seven feet three inches at Brynlliw, does not lend itself easily to fully mechanised longwall mining and considerable geological difficulties caused the management to re-think the system of working. At the time of writing, the colliery is still working, having recently survived a period of threatened closure through further determined efforts by management and men to overcome the inherent mining difficulties.

59. Cynheidre/Pentremawr Colliery, Five Roads, near Llanelli.
The Cynheidre Nos. 1 and 2 Shafts were sunk to 798 and 786 yards respectively during 1954–56. Lying just under two miles south south-west of Pentremawr Colliery, on the flank of the hillside over-looking Pontyates, these shafts provide access to large reserves of deep-lying anthracite coal which could not be economically worked from the crop by the traditional method of slants and drift mines used hitherto in the Gwendraeth Valley. During 1972, 1,430 men produced 472,000 tons from the combined Cynheidre/Pentremawr Colliery from the Big Vein/ Pumpquart Seams. The photograph, taken in 1971, shows the new-style winding towers at Cynheidre.